by Daphne Greaves
illustrated by Lance Lekander

SCHOOL PUBLISHERS

Printed in China

ISBN 10: 0-15-350688-1
ISBN 13: 978-0-15-350688-8

Ordering Options
ISBN 10: 0-15-350600-8 (Grade 3 On-Level Collection)
ISBN 13: 978-0-15-350600-0 (Grade 3 On-Level Collection)
ISBN 10: 0-15-357909-9 (package of 5)
ISBN 13: 978-0-15-357909-7 (package of 5)

2 3 4 5 6 7 8 9 10 985 12 11 10 09 08 07

Setting: The Milky Way Galaxy

Narrator 1: This story takes place in the year 3000, in the Milky Way Galaxy.

Narrator 2: Like most inhabitants of the Milky Way, the Kirk family lives in a functional space station.

Narrator 1: It has everything. There's even a machine that washes, dries, and irons clothes in five minutes. It has ample room for a huge family wash.

Narrator 2: The Kirks have the latest video phone. The person you're talking to is visible on a screen. They also have a cleaning robot to do the housework.

Narrator 1: When robots first came out, everyone felt great amazement.

Narrator 2: Robots used to be scarce, but now everyone has one.

Narrator 1: However, even with all these machines, family life takes a lot of effort. It seems like families are permanently rushed.

Narrator 2: As we'll see, the Kirks are certainly busy. Janey Kirk is in the fourth grade. Her favorite subject is science. Tom is her brother.

Janey: Has anybody seen my biology report?

Tom: You left it on the kitchen table.

Janey: Are you coming to watch the Sunbeams today?

Narrator I: Janey also plays volleyball.

Tom: I can't. I'm leading a painting workshop at the senior center.

Narrator 2: Tom is a very talented artist. He also volunteers at a senior center.

Mom: Nobody leaves home without a decent breakfast.

Narrator I: Mom is a rocket pilot. Every day she flies people from planet to planet. People take the rockets to school and work.

Mom: Everybody sit down. Where's your father?

Janey: Practicing his speech in front of the mirror.

Narrator 1: Dad works for local government.

Narrator 2: He's giving a speech later today.

Tom: Dad, hurry up! Mom just set the meal-maker.

Janey: We're having oatmeal in ten seconds!

Dad: Good morning, everyone. How do I look?

Mom: I think a red tie is better with that shirt.

Dad: Are you sure? I kind of like this blue color.

Narrator 2: Dad is wearing a new kind of tie. You tap it to change the color.

Narrator 1: Now one tie is all anyone needs.

Janey: You and Mom are coming to my game, right?

Dad: I might have to go on the news after my speech.

Mom: I'm going to try, but I'm required to fly the rocket to Zygon this afternoon. That's two galaxies away. I might not get back in time.

Janey: I understand. Flying a rocket is an important responsibility.

Mom: Janey, we all think you're important too.

Janey: I know.

Narrator I: Janey is putting on a brave front, but her emotions are really stirred up.

Tom: Dad, I thought you were wearing the tie red.

Dad: I was just looking at the blue again.

Mom: Red is better.

Dad: Red it is!

Narrator 2: After breakfast, the Kirks begin their day.

Narrator I: Finally, it is time for the volleyball game. Janey's team, the Sunbeams, is playing the Asteroids.

Narrator 1: The gym is filled with cheering fans. A friend on the team has beckoned Janey over.

Sunbeam 1: I'm really excited about the game. My mom is here today.

Sunbeam 2: My parents are here, too.

Sunbeam 1: Janey, where is your family sitting?

Janey: Actually, they might not be able to make it.

Sunbeam 2: Gee, that's too bad. There's the whistle. We're starting.

Narrator 1: Janey looks around the gym, but she doesn't see anyone from her family.

Narrator 2: The coach calls out to Janey.

Coach: Number Ten, we're about to start.

Janey: Yes, Coach!

Narrator 1: The announcers begin to call the game.

Announcer 1: This is going to be a great game.

Announcer 2: Yes, the Sunbeams and Asteroids are both strong teams.

Narrator 2: In the year 3000, volleyball players wear special shoes so that they can jump high. It makes for a very exciting game.

Announcer I: They're ready to start the game! The Asteroids are serving the ball!

Announcer 2: It's high over the net and falling!

Coach: Janey! You take this one!

Janey: Huh? Oops!

Announcer I: Janey Kirk on the Sunbeams let that one go by.

Announcer 2: That's one point for the Asteroids. Number Ten seems a little distracted.

Announcer I: When a player dozes, the other team scores!

11

Narrator 1: Janey is distracted because she keeps looking for her family.

Narrator 2: Suddenly, the ball is spiked high up into the air.

Janey: I've got it!

Narrator 1: This time Janey pushes off in her special shoes. She bounces high up to the ceiling of the gym.

Narrator 2: Then Janey notices something strange out of the corner of her eye. Something in the seats is changing colors from blue to red.

Narrator 1: Janey glances over and sees her father's color tie. Her mother is sitting next to her father.

Narrator 2: Janey's brother, Tom, jumps up from his seat and waves.

Tom: Go, Janey! Go, Sunbeams!

Narrator 2: Janey is so happy that she sails down to the ball and sends it flying back over the net.

Announcer 2: One point for the Sunbeams!

Announcer 1: Way to go Number Ten!

Narrator 1: After the game, Janey's family congratulates her.

Dad: Good game!

Tom: You played great!

Mom: We're so proud of you!

Janey: Thanks! What happened? I thought you couldn't come.

Dad: I juggled a few things.

Tom: I asked one of the seniors to lead the workshop today.

Mom: I switched rockets with another pilot.

Janey: I'm glad you did.

Narrator 1: Whether it's the year 2000 or 3000, families have a lot in common.

Narrator 2: Busy families try hard to make time for one another.

Think Critically

1. What color was Dad's tie when he first came down to breakfast? What color was it next?

2. Why was Janey distracted during her volleyball game?

3. How would you describe Janey's brother, Tom?

4. Why did Janey's mother say she might not be able to go to the game?

5. What are some details from this story that interested you? Why?

 Science

The Milky Way! The Kirk family lives in the Milky Way Galaxy. Go on the Internet or look in a book to find a photograph and information about the Milky Way. Then write a paragraph describing your findings.

School-Home Connection Talk with a family member about time-saving devices like the washing machine in the story. Discuss what kinds of devices you'd like to see invented in the future.

Word Count: 982